ART NOUVEAU ~ DECO

COMPILED BY TONY CURTIS

First Published   1979

Converted at the rate of exchange on the day of sale.

ISBN 902921-87-8

Copyright © Lyle Publications 1979
Published by Lyle Publications, Glenmayne, Galashiels, Selkirkshire, Scotland.
Distributed in the U.S.A. by Apollo, 391 South Road, Poughkeepsie, N.Y. 12601.

INTRODUCTION

Congratulations! You now have in your hands an extremely valuable book. It is one of a series specially devised to aid the busy professional dealer in his everyday trading. It will also prove to be of great value to all collectors and those with goods to sell, for it is crammed with illustrations, brief descriptions and valuations of hundreds of antiques.

Every effort has been made to ensure that each specialised volume contains the widest possible variety of goods in its particular category though the greatest emphasis is placed on the middle bracket of trade goods rather than on those once - in - a - lifetime museum pieces whose values are of academic rather than practical interest to the vast majority of dealers and collectors.

This policy has been followed as a direct consequence of requests from dealers who sensibly realise that, no matter how comprehensive their knowledge, there is always a need for reliable, up-to-date reference works for identification and valuation purposes.

When using your Antiques and their Values to assess the worth of goods, please bear in mind that it would be impossible to place upon any item a precise value which would hold good under all circumstances. No antique has an exactly calculable value; its price is always the result of a compromise reached between buyer and seller, and questions of condition, local demand and the business acumen of the parties involved in a sale are all factors which affect the assessment of an object's 'worth' in terms of hard cash.

In the final analysis, however, such factors cancel out when large numbers of sales are taken into account by an experienced valuer, and it is possible to arrive at a surprisingly accurate assessment of current values of antiques; an assessment which may be taken confidently to be a fair indication of the worth of an object and which provides a reliable basis for negotiation.

Throughout this book, objects are grouped under category headings and, to expedite reference, progress in price order within their own categories. Where the description states 'one of a pair' the value given is that for the pair sold as such.

Printed by Apollo Press, Dominion Way, Worthing, Sussex, England.
Bound by Newdigate Press, Vincent Lane, Dorking, Surrey, England.

CONTENTS

BOXES

Art Nouveau smoker's cabinet with brass facings, circa 1920, 1ft. 9in. high. $95 £48

Oak inlaid stationery box, circa 1905.
$100 £50

Miniature treasure chest in silver, Art Nouveau design, Birmingham, 1904. $110 £55

Primavera 'Longwy' crackle-glazed pottery box and cover, 9.5cm. diameter, 1920's. $133 £70

Reco Capey carved box and cover, 18cm. high.
$465 £240

'Intarsia' brass mounted and inlaid wood casket, circa 1900, 14cm. long.
$505 £260

Reco Capey carved ebony box and cover, 21cm. high.
$505 £260

Madurell gilt metal casket, circa 1900, 37.5cm. long.
$790 £400

Good Gallé marquetry casket, 1890's, 28.5cm. high. $3,920 £2,000

Art Nouveau solid bronze inkwell, circa 1900, 7in. long. $48 £24

Art Nouveau bronze wall panel, 8½ x 5¾in. $50 £25

An Art Nouveau bronze bowl with flowers in relief, 24cm. long. $70 £35

One of a set of five Art Nouveau bronze plaques. $115 £60

Pair of late 19th century bronze vases. $130 £65

One of a pair of Leon Jallot Art Deco bronze appliques, 19.3cm. high, circa 1925. $295 £150

Heyner bronze letter opener, 30cm. long, circa 1900.$295 £150

Hagenauer bronze vase, circa 1910, 11.5cm. high. $335 £170

Bronze and Favrile glass candlestick, by Tiffany, 8in. high. $460 £250

Stylish WMF polished
bronze stemmed dish,
circa 1910, 19cm. high.
$594 £300

Wiener Werkstatte
bronze vase, circa
1910, 8cm. high.
$620 £320

Paignant polychrome
gilt bronze vase, circa
1900, 20.25cm. high.
$480 £260

Gilt metal Art Nouveau
jardiniere, German,
circa 1900, 72cm. wide.
$700 £360

Korschann bronze
vase, 31.5cm. high,
circa 1900.
$785 £400

Gilt bronze group of a
bobsleigh team, circa
1936, 28.5cm. high.
$890 £480

One of a pair of Tiffany
studios gilt bronze candle
holders, circa 1900, 47.5cm.
high. $1,164 £600

One of a pair of Art
Nouveau gilt bronze
jardinieres, circa 1900,
16½in. high.
$1,500 £755

Bronze two-branched
candelabrum, circa
1900, 19¼in. high.
$1,500 £755

Part of a bronze desk set by Tiffany, twelve pieces in all.
$1,000 £505

Part of a rare desk set by Tiffany, six pieces in all.
$1,100 £575

Gilt bronze desk set in the Zodiac pattern by Tiffany, eleven
pieces in all. $1,100 £575

BRONZE FIGURES

A small late 19th century bust of Judith, 7in. high. $120 £60

An Art Nouveau coloured metal figure of a girl and a pillar, on onyx base, 11in. high. $150 £75

Bronze figure of Harry Vardon by Henry Pegram, circa 1908, 14in. high. $155 £85

Late 19th century Russian model of a lady. $180 £90

Bronze and ivory Art Deco figure. $180 £100

Art Nouveau spelter bust, signed, circa 1900. $200 £100

Bronze and ivory Art Deco figure. $200 £110

Spelter figure of a girl on an onyx and marble base, circa 1920, 1ft. 6in. long. $265 £130

Limousin bronze figure, 1930's, 56cm. high. $250 £130

A bronze dancing figure of Isadora Duncan, 18in. high. $405 £200

Art Deco metal figure by Rischmann, 22¾in. high. $390 £200

Stylish bronze figure of a vulture, 20cm. high, 1920's. $390 £210

Art Deco bronze nude dancer signed Bouraine, 23in. high. $485 £240

Philippe gilt bronze figure of a woman, 1920's, 56cm. high. $445 £240

Bronze and ivory figure of a young woman, 26.75cm. high. $465 £250

Lorenzl bronze and ivory figure, 1930's, 29.75cm. high. $480 £260

Large Art Deco spelter group, 32in. wide, Paris. $505 £260

Bronze figure of a dancing girl, signed Lorenzl, circa 1920, 16in. high. $500 £260

13

BRONZE FIGURES

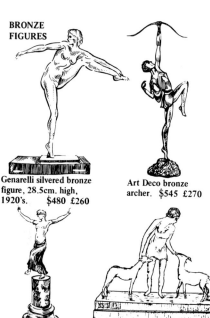

Genarelli silvered bronze figure, 28.5cm. high, 1920's. $480 £260

Art Deco bronze archer. $545 £270

Rigot bronze and ivory figure, 1920's, 35cm. high. $520 £280

Barthelemy bronze and ivory dancing girl, 26.5cm. high. $560 £300

Art Deco group in silvered bronze. $605 £300

Italian bronze figure of a dancer, signed G. Beneduce. $605 £300

Rigot bronze and ivory figure, 35cm. high, 1920's. $580 £300

Bronze and ivory Art Deco figure. $560 £310

Bouraine silvered bronze figure, 1920's, 47.5cm. high. $620 £320

14

Art Deco bronze and ivory group of a seated female with two dogs.
$645 £320

Art Deco ivory and bronze figure by Gregoire.
$655 £325

Art Deco bronze group by Gemaretti, 22in. wide. $680 £350

Automobiles Ferman, a bronze figure of Daedelus on a marble base fitted with two inkwells by G. Colin, 1907. $780 £385

Raoul Larche bronze bust, circa 1900, 47cm. high. $775 £400

Art Deco can-can figure on a marble base. $770 £400

Bronze and ivory figure of a dancer in theatrical costume. $910 £450

A stylish Art Deco bronze by Le Faguays.
$910 £450

Art Nouveau bronze, 21in. high. $950 £480

BRONZE FIGURES

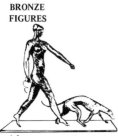

A bronze group of a woman and a greyhound, by R. Rivoire, 1925.
$1,090 £540

Bronze and ivory figure of a dancer by Philippe, 16½in. high. $1,170 £650

Art Deco bronze and ivory group of a horse with young girl attendant, on an onyx base, 1ft.3in. wide.
$1,515 £750

A fine Art Nouveau ivory and bronze figure, signed Gerdago, 12in. high.
$1,515 £750

Stylish Bouraine silvered bronze figure, 37.5cm. high, 1930's. $1,575 £850

Barrias gilt bronze figure, 1890's, 43cm. high. $1,760 £950

Good Bouraine green patinated bronze figure, 52cm. high, 1930's. $1,760 £950

Colinet bronze and ivory dancing girl, 43.25cm. high. $1,850 £1,000

Stylish Guigner Art Deco gilt bronze group, 54.75cm. high, 1930's. $2,590 £1,400

16

Art Deco bronze and ivory figure of a fan-dancer by Philippe, 18½in. high.
$2,520 £1,400

Painted bronze and ivory group by Prof. Poertzel, on marble base, 48cm. high.$4,275 £2,250

Flamand bronze Art Nouveau figure of a woman, 59cm. high, circa 1900.
$5,180 £2,800

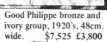

Colinet bronze and ivory figure of a dancer, 1920's, 43.5cm. high.$5,430 £2,800

Good Philippe bronze and ivory group, 1920's, 48cm. wide. $7,525 £3,800

Silver bronze figure of a woman, circa 1906. $7,700 £3,850

Large Philippe bronze and ivory figure, 64.5cm. high, 1920's.
$7,810 £4,200

One of a series of 'Scarf Game' dancers, circa 1901.
$12,100 £6,455

Gilded bronze figure of the dancer Loie Fuller, 17¾in. high.
$13,535 £7,200

BRONZE CHIPARUS FIGURES

Chiparus gilt bronze figure, 40.5cm. high, 1920's. £775 £420

Painted metal Chiparus group of woman and goats. $1,110 £550

Chiparus bronze and ivory figure, 34.5cm. high. $1,115 £600

Chiparus bronze and ivory figure of a young woman, 36.5cm. high, 1920's. $1,480 £800

Chiparus silvered and gilt bronze figure, 1920's, 46cm. long. $1,940 £1,000

Chiparus bronze and ivory figure, 41cm. high, 1920's. $1,850 £1,000

Bronze and ivory figure by D. H. Chiparus, 11¾in. high. $1,980 £1,100

Bronze and ivory group by D. H. Chiparus, 11¼in. high. $2,070 £1,150

Bronze and ivory female figure by Chiparus. $2,425 £1,200

CHIPARUS FIGURES

Small Chiparus bronze and ivory cat-suit girl, 37.5cm. high, 1920's. $2,500 £1,350

Chiparus bronze and ivory figure, 10½in. long, 1920's. $3,105 £1,600

Bronze and ivory figure of a dancer by D. H. Chiparus, 15½in. high. $2,880 £1,600

Chiparus bronze and ivory figure, 56.25cm. high, 1920's. $3,330 £1,800

Bronze and ivory figure of a dancer by Chiparus, 44cm. high. $2,970 £1,650

Chiparus bronze and ivory dancer. $4,240 £2,100

An exotic ivory and bronze figure of a dancer, 16in. high, signed Chiparus. $4,400 £2,200

Chiparus bronze and ivory figure, 58cm. high, 1920's. $4,070 £2,200

Bronze and ivory figure by Demetre Chiparus. $10,505 £5,200

19

BRONZE
PREISS FIGURES

Preiss bronze and ivory figure of 'The Bathing Girl', on marble base, 1930's, 9¼in. high.
$990 £550

Preiss bronze and ivory figure of a schoolboy, 21cm. high.$1,080 £580

Bronze and ivory figure of 'The Sunworshipper' by Preiss, 1930's, 18.5cm. high. $1,100 £600

Preiss bronze and ivory figure, 20cm. high, 1930's. $1,265 £680

Preiss bronze and ivory figure of 'The Skater', 1930's, 35.5cm. high.
$1,490 £800

An Art Nouveau ivory and bronze figure of a woman throwing a javelin. $1,820 £900

Preiss figure of a standing girl in a casual dress.
$1,820 £900

Ivory and gilt bronze figure of a running girl by F. Preiss.
$1,820 £900

Art Deco bronze and ivory figure of an air-woman, by F. Preiss.
$2,420 £1,200

Preiss bronze and
ivory figure, 29.5cm.
high, 1920's.
$2,230 £1,200

Ivory and bronze
figure 'Invocation'
by Preiss.
$2,420 £1,200

Bronze 'Flute Player'
by F. Preiss, 17¾in.
high. $2,425 £1,200

'Con Brio' gilt bronze
and ivory female fig-
ure by F. Preiss.
$2,425 £1,200

Preiss bronze and ivory
lampstand, 1930's,
55.5cm. high, on marble
base. $2,590 £1,400

Bronze and ivory fig-
ure of the 'Torch Dan-
cer' by Preiss, 15¾in.
tall. $3,110 £1,540

'The Balloon Girl'
by F. Preiss, on
onyx base.
$4,240 £2,100

Good Preiss bronze and
ivory dancing girl,
37.25cm. high.
$4,090 £2,200

Bronze and ivory
figure by F. Preiss,
14¾in. high.
$9,600 £5,000

21

CAR MASCOTS

Standing figure of the Esso man, 5½in. high, on a radiator cap.
$135 £75

Chromium plated Minerva. $200 £100

Lalique Vitesse mascot.
$505 £250

Glass car mascot entitled 'Spirit of the Wind' by Rene Lalique, 10¼in. long. $705 £350

Lalique cockerel's head. $705 £350

Lalique Dragon-fly mascot.
$755 £375

Lalique Falcon mascot.
$810 £400

Lalique glass Longchamps mascot. $810 £450

Lalique glass car mascot, 1920's, 14cm. wide.
$1,980 £1,000

A Devonmoor pottery earthenware bowl, with applied and incised decoration. $30 £15

Unusual amphora glazed earthenware basket, circa 1910, 20.5cm. high. $60 £32

Ruskin eggshell pottery bowl, circa 1910. $130 £65

Stoneware foliate bowl by Charles Vyse, 7¼in. diam. $115 £65

Stoneware foliate bowl by Charles Vyse, with shaped rim, 7¼in. diam. $115 £65

Stoneware bowl by Lucy Rie, 11¾in. diam. $160 £90

Moorcroft pottery bowl decorated with chrysanthemums. $200 £100

Wedgwood Fairy lustre ware bowl. $810 £400

Wedgwood Fairyland lustre bowl, 1920's, 11in. diam. $1,285 £680

CHINA
CHARGERS

Early Fulham period
De Morgan copper
lustre small plate,
6¾in. diameter.
$90 £50

De Morgan copper
lustre small plate,
6¾in. diameter.
$145 £80

Fulham period De
Morgan ruby lustre
charger, 11¾in.
diam. $230 £120

De Morgan copper
lustre charger,
14¼in. diameter.
$325 £180

De Morgan copper
lustre charger,
14½in. diameter.
$425 £220

William De Morgan
copper lustre, ochre
charger, 12¼in.
diameter.$465 £240

Fulham period De
Morgan ochre lustre
charger, 11¾in.
diameter.$815 £420

One of a pair of early
Martin Brothers wall
plates, 13¼in. diam.
$1,010 £500

Clement Massier lustre
charger, circa 1900,
48cm. diameter.
$2,575 £1,300

Royal Dux figure,
9in. long, 6in.
high. $160 £80

De Morgan lustre dish
by Charles Passenger,
14¼in. diameter, 1888-
97. $240 £130

Limoges enamelled
pot and cover, 1920's,
11.5cm., by Sarlandie.
$275 £150

Theodore Deck dish,
13¼in. diameter,
circa 1880.
$295 £150

Royal Dux dish of
two lovers, circa
1910, 30.5cm. high.
$380 £210

Turn Art Nouveau
ceramic dish, Aust-
rian, circa 1900,
44cm. long.
$514 £260

Pottery centrepiece of
gondola form by Kataro
Shirayamadani, 41cm.
long, circa 1888.
$660 £340

A Zsolnay lustre dish,
30cm. wide, circa 1900.
$810 £400

Fine porcelain centre-
piece, 37½in. long,
painted K.P.M.
$1,760 £920

CHINA FIGURES

Royal Doulton figure of a Churchillian bulldog, circa 1940, 6in. high. $100 £55

Poole pottery fish glazed in green with a black base, 17in. high. $120 £60

Royal Doulton figure of a fox, 7in. high, circa 1937.
$120 £65

Paris porcelain figure of a woman, 31.8cm. high, circa 1920.
$125 £65

19th century Royal Dux group of a child playing with a dog.
$130 £65

Wiener Werkstatte glazed earthenware figure, circa 1910, 29cm. high.
$195 £100

Terracotta portrait bust by Laure Hayman, 1920, 59cm. high. $245 £125

Issy high-fired porcelain figure, 1913, 44cm. high. $395 £200

Doulton stoneware owl tobacco jar and cover, 7½in. high, circa 1895. $390 £210

Rosenthal porcelain group of a young woman and a fawn, 34cm. high, 1930's.
$425 £220

Pair of Goldscheider book-ends, 1930's, 21cm. high.
$490 £250

Boulogne crackle glazed pottery figure, 61cm. high, 1920's. $570 £300

Boulogne glazed pottery figure, 47.5cm. high, 1925.$610 £320

Meissen porcelain figure, 30.5cm. high, 1930's. $660 £340

Charles Vyse figure of 'Barnet Fair', circa 1933, 10¼in. high.
$630 £340

Royal Doulton figure of 'Miss 1927'.
$750 £370

Art Deco female figure by Erdago.
$810 £400

One of a pair of Royal Dux busts of girls, circa 1910, 47.6cm. and 48.8cm. high.
$1,080 £600

Royal Doulton art
pot about 1902-22,
7½in. high x 8½in.
deep. $30 £15

Minton art pot, dating
between 1895-1900 in
a single shade of mint
green, 8½in. high.
$56 £28

Victorian hanging art
pot by the Watcombe
Pottery Co., about
1867-1901, 7in. high
x 9in. deep. $70 £35

Doulton (Lambeth)
art pot, about 1880-
91, 8½in. high x
10in. deep. $85 £42

A Royal Doulton pat-
tern relief moulded
lily pattern jardiniere
signed M.B., 9in. high.
$90 £45

Art Deco pot by Thos.
Forester & Sons Ltd.,
Staffs, about 1930,
7½in. high x 8½in.
deep. $100 £50

A Doulton jar-
diniere stand.
$130 £65

An Ault jardiniere
designed by Christo-
pher Dresser.
$140 £70

Attractive Art Nouveau
Minton jardiniere,
about 1900-08, 12½in.
high x 14½in. deep.
$180 £90

Doulton jardiniere
with near matching
stand. $275 £135

A Victorian Bretby ear-
thenware jardiniere and
matching pedestal.
$285 £140

An Art Nouveau jar-
diniere and stand by
Bretby. $300 £150

Martin Brothers jar-
diniere, 7¼in. high,
dated 1900, incised
signature.$370 £200

Burmantofts jardiniere
and stand, 37½in. high,
circa 1900. $350 £180

Massive Liberty & Co.
earthenware jardiniere,
76cm. diam., circa
1905. $405 £220

Doulton stoneware jar-
diniere and stand,
39¾in. high, circa
1900. $500 £270

A decorative glazed
ceramic jardiniere,
circa 1900.
$605 £300

Early 20th century large
Doulton stoneware jar-
diniere and stand, 54½in.
high. $1,665 £850

29

CHINA JUGS

An unmarked pottery hot water jug. $8 £4

Royal Doulton floral toilet jug. $20 £10

Poole pottery unglazed jug, 8in. high, 1930. $50 £25

Martin Brothers stoneware pitcher. $110 £55

Doulton silicon 'leatherware' jug and matching pair of mugs, London 1902. $140 £70

Cadinen glazed earthenware jug, 1910-20, 19.75cm. high. $140 £75

Doulton stoneware jug, 9in. high, circa 1900. $295 £160

Doulton stoneware silver mounted cycling jug and two beakers, circa 1900. $220 £120

Martin Brothers stoneware jug, 9¾in. high, incised signature, dated 1895. $370 £200

Art Deco tea-
pot in shape of
a car. $60 £30

Porzellan-Manufaktur-
Burgau porcelain coffee
pot, 20cm. high, circa
1910. $110 £60

William Moorcroft
teapot 1898, pain-
ted with blue poppies.
$120 £60

A Clarice Cliff 'Bizarre' tea service,
twenty-four pieces, 1930's. $205 £100

Attractive Clarice Cliff 'Bizarre'
teapot and cream jug, 1930's.
$196 £100

A Limoges porcelain coffee service
designed by Jean Luce, 1920's.
      $355 £175

'Bizarre' painted glazed pottery break-
fast set, 1930's. $390 £200

CHINA VASES

Clarice Cliff 'Bizarre' vase, 20.5cm. high, 1930's. $68 £35

Bretby pottery vase with turquoise blue glazed medallions.
$150 £75

Villeroy and Boch vase, circa 1910, 45.5cm. high.
$198 £100

Quimper Art Deco decorated stoneware vase, 18cm. high, 1920's. $190 £100

Limoges porcelain vase by L. Bernardaud & Cie, 15.4cm. high, circa 1923. $230 £120

Florian vase made at MacIntyres, circa 1893.
$255 £125

Small Rozenberg vase, circa 1900, 11cm. high. $270 £140

One of a pair of Doulton stoneware vases, 11¼in. high, circa 1905.
$280 £150

Massive Art Nouveau glazed earthenware jug, circa 1900, 92.1cm. high.$390 £200

32

One of a pair of Moor-
croft vases, 10¾in.
high, circa 1916-21.
$280 £150

Metal mounted D'Argyl
Art Deco decorated
earthenware vase, 28cm.
high, 1920's. $425 £220

De Morgan copper
lustre vase, 10in.
high. $415 £230

Delvaux Paris porcelain
Art Deco vase, circa
1925, 31.5cm. high.
$595 £300

One of a pair of Royal
Doulton stoneware
vases, 14in. high, dated
for 1902. $555 £300

Wiener Werkstatte
glazed earthenware
triple vase, 23cm.
high, circa 1910/20.
$1,125 £580

One of a pair of Wedgwood
Fairyland lustre 'Candlemas'
vases, 8½in. high, 1920's.
$1,510 £800

Rozenberg porcelain
vase, circa 1890.
$1,685 £850

Jean Dunand egg-
shell lacquer vase,
circa 1925, 23.5cm.
high. $1,980 £1,000

33

An oak case grand-
mother musical
chiming clock.
$120 £60

Late 19th century
Art Deco clock in
an oak case.
$220 £110

A stylish modernist clock,
circa 1930, 112cm. high,
in black painted wood.
$277 £140

Wrought iron long-
case clock, circa
1920, 65½in. high.
$590 £300

Wickerwork long-
case clock.
$1,370 £700

Edwardian chiming
grandfather clock
in a mahogany case,
9ft. tall.
$3,240 £1,620

A combined time-piece, barometer and calendar in a silver mounted case. $50 £25

Art Deco mantel timepiece in marble case, by Maple & Co., Paris, 6¼in. high. $90 £45

A timepiece in mahogany inlaid upright shaped case, 12in. high. $93 £46

Liberty & Co. 'Tudric' pewter clock, after 1903, 17cm. high. $175 £95

Art Deco soft metal mantel clock in the form of a female figure. $200 £100

Art Nouveau clock signed N. Bochin. $200 £100

Liberty & Co. 'Tudric' pewter and enamel clock after 1903, 18.75cm. high. $240 £130

Pewter and enamel clock, circa 1905, 14.25cm. high. $260 £140

Silver plated French clock depicting Loie Fuller, circa 1910. $305 £150

CLOCKS
MANTEL

Art Deco bronze
and marble clock,
26cm. wide, 1920's.
$330 £170

Small Liberty & Co. pew-
ter and enamel clock,
19.75cm. high, after 1903.
$335 £180

Art Deco mirror glass
clock, 1930's, 33.75cm.
long. $370 £200

Clock case in green mar-
ble surmounted by a
bronze figure, circa 1900,
39cm. $405 £220

Silver and parcel gilt clock
by Goldsmiths & Silver-
smiths Ltd., London, 1929,
13.5cm. high. $505 £260

Art Nouveau silvered
metal clock case,
circa 1900, 53cm.
high. $545 £280

Continental carved wood
Art Nouveau clock case,
circa 1900, 37.5cm. high.
$590 £320

Cartier breast
pocket clip watch,
1930's, 5.3cm.
$815 £420

Copper and satinised
steel clock, 1930's,
31cm. high.
$855 £440

Large Liberty & Co. 'Tudric' pewter and enamel clock, after 1903, 32cm. high. $890 £480

Bronze and ormolu mantel clock, 12in. wide. $1,080 £600

Liberty & Co. 'Tudric' pewter and enamel clock, circa 1903, 13.5cm. high. $1,110 £600

Preiss clock with marble base, 1930's, 37cm. high. $1,176 £600

Lalique glass 'Siren' clock, circa 1925, 27.5cm. high. $1,570 £850

Preiss bronze and ivory figure of a kneeling dancer supporting a clock. $1,710 £950

Viennese enamelled copper clock, 39cm. high, circa 1910. $2,940 £1,500

Good Lalique glass clock 'Le jour et la nuit', 38.75cm. wide, 1920's. $8,360 £4,400

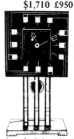

Domino clock by Charles Rennie Mackintosh, circa 1917, 10in. high. $13,130 £6,500

37

An Art Deco soft metal clock set, complete with side urns. $240 £120

Bronze figure on onyx clock set, 21½in. long, circa 1920. $355 £175

Late 19th century painted spelter and onyx clock garniture. $385 £210

Late 19th century spelter and onyx clock garniture, signed Detourbet.
$420 £220

Art Nouveau patinated metal clock garniture, circa 1900. $784 £400

Enamel and gilt bronze clock set by Tiffany. $1,100 £550

Brass water jug with Art Nouveau decoration, circa 1900. $28 £14

Stylish brass jardiniere about 1900, with three supports and pierced work band round the body. $44 £22

Newlyn copper rose bowl, 10¾in. diam., circa 1910. $55 £30

John Pearson copper dish, 17in. diameter, circa 1904. $85 £45

Newlyn School, copper cigar box, sold with a copper bowl, circa 1904. $85 £45

Art Nouveau brass coal bucket with lid and liner, circa 1895. $90 £45

A pair of W. Benson brass candleholders, circa 1900. $120 £65

One of a pair of copper candlesticks, signed Rathbone, 4½in. high, circa 1910. $165 £90

W. Benson copper and brass kettle and burner, 11½in. high, 1890's. $175 £95

COPPER AND BRASS

Copper and brass tobacco jar by Omar Ramsden, circa 1925, 7¼in. high. $185 £100

One of a pair of Liberty & Co. brass candlesticks, 13.5cm. high, circa 1900. $185 £100

English brass and copper covered pitcher, circa 1900, 15¼in. high. $264 £138

One of a pair of Christopher Dresser brass candlesticks, 1880's. $280 £150

Japanese Art Nouveau Zeit Geist cloisonne vase, with damaged base, 46cm. high. $305 £150

John Paul Cooper copper rose bowl, 7½in. diam., early 20th century. $410 £220

Faure enamelled copper vase, 17cm. high, 1930's. $485 £260

Good Wiener Werkstatte tea service, circa 1910, 33.5cm. wide. $3,492 £1,800

One of a pair of patinated and electroplated copper Christofle vases, 26.5cm. high, 1920's. $814 £420

40

A 'Mouseman' oak bed made by Robert Thompson of Kilburn. $400 £200

Walnut half-tester bed, circa 1900, 83in. x 58¼in. $600 £310

Mahogany and burr walnut double bed by Louis Majorelle, circa 1897, 68½in. wide.
    $10,000 £5,050

BOOKCASES

Small Edwardian inlaid mahogany open fronted set of two shelves. $40 £20

Stained beechwood book cabinet, 27in. wide, 1890's.
    $110 £60

Art Nouveau mahogany secretaire bookcase, 48in. wide. $1,500 £750

BUFFETS

Mercier Freres walnut and ivory bedside table, early 1920's, 63cm. high. $295 £150

Mahogany buffet, circa 1895, 64in. high. $880 £455

Fine Art Nouveau walnut buffet, English, circa 1900, 68½in. wide.
    $2,200 £1,180

FURNITURE
CABINETS

Late 19th century carved oak coal cabinet with brass handles.
$46 £25

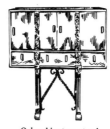

Oak cabinet on stand, 42in. wide, circa 1910-20. $225 £120

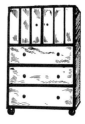

Oak cupboard by Heal & Sons, circa 1905. $305 £150

Liberty & Co. tall oak side cabinet, circa 1920, 26in. wide. $490 £250

Small Art Nouveau breakfront cabinet, circa 1900, 58in. wide. $550 £285

Mahogany cabinet, circa 1895, 68½in. high. $660 £340

Wood and vellum cabinet by C. Bugatti, circa 1900.
$810 £400

Stylish 1930's cocktail cabinet in pale walnut, 144cm. wide. $1,176 £600

Painted oak corner cupboard, 84in. high, 1880's. $1,210 £600

A silvered wood cabinet by Waring & Gillow, circa 1930, after a design by Chermayeff.
$1,615 £800

Walnut and burr elm cabinet by Russell, circa 1928.
$1,615 £800

A fruitwood marquetry cabinet by Louis Majorelle.
$2,020 £1,000

An Art Nouveau style marquetry inlaid walnut cabinet, 5ft.6in. high.
$2,020 £1,000

Eugene Printz patinated bronze and lacquered wood cabinet, 1930's, 109cm. high.
$2,375 £1,200

Fruitwood marquetry display cabinet by Majorelle, circa 1910, 64cm. wide.
$2,325 £1,200

Fine mahogany cabinet by Louis Majorelle, circa 1900, 30½in. wide.
$2,530 £1,305

Oak cabinet by Charles Rennie Mackintosh, circa 1905. $3,535 £1,750

Early 20th century Italian table cabinet by Carlo Bugatti.
$12,120 £6,000

Edwardian mahogany corner chair with box-wood string inlay.
$100 £50

Edwardian mahogany elbow chair with box-wood string inlay and upholstered seat.
$100 £50

Edwardian mahogany elbow chair with a pierced back splat and cabriole legs.
$130 £65

Decorative chair, attributed to Carlo Bugatti, circa 1910, 74cm. high.
$130 £70

A mahogany Art Nouveau arm chair, on square tapering legs.
$150 £75

One of a pair of Art Deco gilt wood chairs, 94cm. high.
$150 £75

Edwardian inlaid mahogany elbow chair on cabriole legs.
$140 £75

Mahogany arm chair, 1890's, on turned legs.
$165 £90

Stained beechwood arm chair, circa 1890.
$175 £95

One of a set of six
oak dining chairs,
circa 1900.
$225 £120

Large Art Deco gilt
wood tub chair,
early 1920's.
$395 £200

One of a pair of
Art Deco gilt wood
arm chairs, early
1920's. $445 £225

One of a pair of oak
chairs, by Charles
Rennie Mackintosh,
circa 1900, 112cm.
high. $480 £260

Part of a beechwood
drawingroom suite,
1890's. $505 £260

One of a set of
six chairs by
Thompson of
Kilburn. $540 £300

One of a pair of oak
open arm chairs,
circa 1900, 31in. high.
$600 £305

One of a pair of
Art Deco tub chairs,
early 1920's.
$590 £310

Asko fibreglass
'globe' chair,
1966, 125cm. diam.
$790 £400

FURNITURE
CHAIRS

One of a set of six
oak dining chairs,
circa 1900. $1,190 £595

An ebonised chair
by Charles Rennie
Mackintosh.
$1,190 £595

A small straight-back
chair in ebonised
wood, designed by
Charles Rennie Mac-
kintosh, 40in. high.
$3,080 £1,540

One of two walnut
and mahogany chairs
sold with a matching
kidney-shaped dressing
table. $4,000 £2,020

One of a pair of Art
Deco rosewood arm
chairs, French, circa
1930. $4,950 £2,550

One of a pair of arm
chairs by Jacques
Rhulmann, circa
1925. $6,380 £3,430

Black and white wooden
prototype chair as desig-
ned by Gerrit Rietveld,
circa 1917.
$10,590 £5,880

An elegant chair by Charles
Rennie Mackintosh, made
for the owner of the Willow
Tea Rooms, Glasgow.
$20,200 £10,000

Lacquered wood
chair by Eileen
Gray.
$24,040 £12,355

Art Deco burl maple chest of drawers, circa 1925, 51¾in. wide. $440 £225

English oak chest of drawers, 39in. wide, circa 1930. $520 £280

Art Deco burl maple chest of drawers, 63¾in. high. $990 £510

COUCHES

An oak and beaten copper inlaid settle, circa 1905. $360 £180

Mahogany corner settee, circa 1900, 53¼in. $385 £210

Part of a three-piece suite of Art Deco silvered furniture. $1,575 £780

A superb gondola sofa by Marcel Goard. $28,000 £14,000

47

FURNITURE
DESKS

Edwardian maho-
gany fall front
secretaire, 23in.
wide. $160 £80

An Edwardian maho-
gany and satinwood
writing table in the
Art Nouveau style.
$605 £300

Early 20th century
satinwood bonheur
du jour, 29¾in. wide.
$715 £370

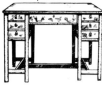

Walnut desk inlaid
with various woods
by Daneway, circa
1910. $810 £400

20th century oak double-
sided desk made from
16th century panelling,
6ft.7½in. long.
$1,225 £680

Walnut secretaire
by Peter Van Der
Waals.
$3,990 £2,100

DOORS

A pair of Rowley Gallery silvered
wood doors, 1920's, 216cm. high.
$396 £200

Pair of doors by Jean Dunand for a
Normandie liner. $12,295 £6,470

48

Late 19th century
mahogany display
cabinet with mirrored
back and cabriole legs.
$180 £90

Edwardian bow fronted
inlaid mahogany china
cabinet with two shelves
enclosed by glazed
leaded doors. $285 £140

An inlaid mahogany
china cabinet with
domed cornice, 4ft.
wide, 6ft.2in. high.
$295 £145

Late 19th century maho-
gany display cabinet with
a mirrored back.
$305 £150

Edwardian inlaid
mahogany china
cabinet, 28in. wide.
$305 £150

An Edwardian maho-
gany display cabinet,
with mirror backed
central and lower scroll
backed glazed side cup-
boards. $355 £175

Edwardian inlaid maho-
gany display cupboard
with glazed doors.
$355 £175

Mahogany display
cabinet, 43½in. wide,
circa 1900.$425 £230

Mahogany vitrine,
circa 1895, 68in.
high. $660 £340

49

FURNITURE
DISPLAY CABINETS

Art Nouveau mahogany and inlaid display cabinet, 4ft.5in. wide. $690 £360

An Art Nouveau library cabinet, the copper frieze at the top inscribed 'Reading Maketh A Full Man'. $810 £400

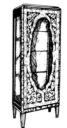

Early 1920's Art Deco walnut and gilt wood vitrine, 172cm. high. $790 £400

Edwardian display cabinet inlaid with rosewood, stamped Edwards & Roberts. $845 £470

Art Nouveau mahogany side cabinet, circa 1900, 53in. wide. $940 £490

Superior Art Nouveau style inlaid mahogany china cabinet, 3ft.6in. wide. $1,110 £550

Mahogany display cabinet, 46in. wide, circa 1900. $1,395 £750

Austrian display cabinet, circa 1900-10, 125.5cm. wide. $1,560 £800

Marquetry display stand by Emile Galle. $3,905 £2,100

50

DRESSING TABLES

FURNITURE

High Kitsch dressing table, 161cm. high, 1930's.
$505 £260

A walnut and mahogany kidney-shaped dressing table, sold with two matching chairs. $4,000 £2,020

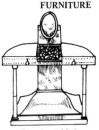

Dressing table by Emile Jacques Rhulmann, circa 1920, 43½in. wide.
$13,445 £6,655

PIANOS

Oak Bechstein upright piano by Walter Cave, circa 1900, 56in. wide.
$650 £350

Art Nouveau piano by Broadwood.
$1,210 £600

Sycamore cased baby grand by Strohmenger.
$2,725 £1,350

SCREENS

Early 20th century beechwood firescreen with needlework panel. $40 £20

American leaded glass firescreen, circa 1900, 45¼in. high.
$2,860 £1,537

Rare and fine stained glass firescreen by Tiffany, 57½in. wide.
$7,700 £4,030

51

Art Deco sideboard
in amboyna wood,
5ft.2in. long.$90 £45

Small sideboard in
pale walnut, 1930's,
136.5cm. wide.
$345 £175

Large sideboard in
pale walnut, 1930's,
175cm. wide.
$345 £175

A yew wood dres-
ser, probably
American, 1900-25,
5ft.7in. wide.
$450 £225

Eric Sharpe sideboard
with plate glass top,
54in. long.
$670 £360

Fumed oak sideboard
by Thompson of
Kilburn. $740 £410

Fine small oak and
boxwood sideboard
by Gillows & Co.
$2,325 £1,250

An Art Nouveau maho-
gany sideboard cupboard,
French, circa 1900, 59in.
wide. $6,000 £3,030

Ebonised sideboard with
silver plated mounts,
about 1875.
$13,130 £6,500

Art Nouveau style
oak hall stand.
$70 £35

A late 19th century pottery
jardiniere stand decorated
with female figures, 3ft. high.
$90 £45

Late 19th century
pine washstand.
$100 £50

Edwardian shaving
stand with an ad-
justable mirror.
$100 £50

Early 1920's wrought
iron and marble guer-
idon, 86.5cm. high.
$295 £150

Early 1920's wrought
iron and marble guer-
idon, 109.5cm. high.
$295 £150

Syrie Maugham painted
wood table or jardiniere,
circa 1936, 93.75cm.
wide. $530 £280

Two-tiered rosewood
jardiniere stand, circa
1895, 16in. square.
$1,500 £755

Art Deco chrome and
mirror coatrack with
umbrella stand, circa
1925. $1,870 £965

Part of a stained mahogany marquetry and ivory inlaid suite, circa 1900.
$230 £120

Suite of tubular chromed metal cantilever seat furniture, 1930's, 80cm. high.
$350 £180

Edwardian inlaid mahogany three-piece suite on short tapered legs with spade
feet. $400 £200

A fine Edwardian mahogany drawingroom suite comprising two arm chairs, a
set of four dining chairs and a 4ft. settee, on cabriole front legs. $405 £200

Edwardian rosewood inlaid drawingroom suite of armed settee and two easy chairs and four inlaid single chairs (seven pieces in all). $655 £325

A 1930's tubular steel three-piece suite. $740 £400

Edwardian carved mahogany drawingroom suite comprising an arm settee, two easy chairs and four single chairs. $910 £450

Suite of Art Nouveau walnut seat furniture, circa 1900, 48in. wide.
     $3,080 £1,585

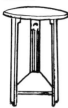

Edwardian oak
occasional table.
$30 £15

Edwardian oval two-
tier oak table with
two side tiers.
$60 £30

Brass mirror-topped
table, circa 1900,
73cm. high.
$155 £80

Three-tier coffee
table in pale walnut
1930's, 91.5cm. wide.
$195 £100

Early 1920's marble
topped Art Deco
occasional table,
54.5cm. square.
$200 £100

Early 1920's oval
mahogany table,
85cm. wide.
$200 £100

Syrie Maugham pain-
ted wood occasional
table, circa 1936,
66.5cm. high.
$245 £130

Art furniture design
two-tier table in
ebony and specimen
wood, circa 1880.
$295 £145

Renouvin Art Deco
music stool, 78.25cm.
wide. $305 £160

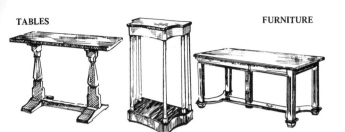

'Mouseman' oak buffet table, 60in. long, 1936-40.$295 £160

Wood and perspex consol table, 1930's, 91.25cm. high. $325 £170

Oak dining table by J. J. Joass, 66in. long, circa 1940. $355 £190

Scandinavian inlaid low table, 1920's, 91.5cm. diameter. $480 £260

French mahogany centre table, circa 1900, 36in. wide. $600 £305

An English brass-mounted 'Odeonesque' occasional table. $655 £325

Oak domino table by Charles Rennie Mackintosh, 79cm. high, circa 1911. $960 £520

Rosewood and mahogany bedside table, by Louis Majorelle, 37½in. high. $1,200 £605

American mahogany dining table and set of chairs, circa 1900. $1,430 £735

Marquetry two-tier
table by Emile
Galle, circa 1890,
26in. square.
$1,500 £755

Rosewood quatre-lobed
etagere by Emile Galle,
circa 1895, 24in. wide.
$1,500 £755

English walnut dining
table, 60½in. diam.,
circa 1935.
$1,415 £760

Attractive shagreen-
covered side table,
1920's, 40cm. high.
$790 £400

Galle fruitwood marquetry
occasional table, circa 1900,
78cm. wide. $1,780 £900

Set of four marque-
try tables with glass
tops, circa 1900, by
Galle. $2,330 £1,200

Rosewood coffee table
by Jacques Rhulmann,
circa 1925, 26½in. diam.
$2,860 £1,535

Emile Jacques Rhul-
mann table, 74.5cm.
wide, circa 1925.
$3,465 £1,750

Fine lacquered wood
and chrome consol
by Donald Desky,
circa 1927, 72in. wide.
$4,620 £2,485

An Edwardian mahogany wardrobe, 7ft. x 5ft. wide.
$355 £175

Part of a fine four-piece bedroom suite. $415 £205

Early 1920's walnut and ivory wardrobe, designed by Leon Jallot, 183cm. high.
$595 £300

'Mouseman' oak cupboard, 36in. wide, circa 1936-40.
$855 £460

A gentleman's wardrobe in oak by Peter Waals, circa 1935.
$1,515 £750

Heal's wardrobe of 1898.
$2,230 £1,150

Stained oak wardrobe by Charles Rennie Mackintosh, circa 1890.
$3,030 £1,500

Solid walnut breakfront wardrobe by Peter Waals.
$4,200 £2,100

Rosewood armoire by Louis Majorelle, 103in. high.
$9,000 £4,545

GLASS
BOWLS

19th century Lalique glass bowl of clear and opaque white glass, 10in. diam. $90 £45

French Lalique glass bowl on four feet, 24cm. diameter, chipped. $100 £50

A Galle cameo glass bowl, the pale pink body overlaid in green and etched with teasels, 19cm. wide. $365 £180

A glass bowl by Gabriel Argy Rousseau. $425 £210

Iridescent Favrile glass flower bowl by Tiffany, 13in. diam. $460 £235

Heavy Walter pate de verre stemmed bowl, 15cm. high, 1920's. $590 £320

Walter pate de verre figure of a peahen, 19cm. long, 1920's. $705 £380

Fine quality bowl by Francois-Emile Decorchemont. $1,080 £540

Rare mounted cameo glass wall flower bowl, 13in. diameter. $1,650 £865

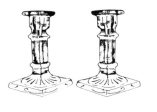

Edwardian moulded glass candlesticks. $4 £2

Pair of 20th century moulded glass candlesticks. $10 £5

Art Deco red and clear glass candlestick. $24 £12

One of a pair of Lalique four-light candelabra, 9½in. high.
$1,080 £600

Pair of Tiffany bronze and glass candlesticks, 14½in. high.
$3,030 £1,500

Fine bronze and iridescent Favrile glass six-branched candelabrum by Tiffany, 15in. high.
$3,500 £1,765

CUPS

Early 20th century green and clear glass cup with silver rim.
$12 £6

One of a set of four Tiffany iridescent glass mugs, circa 1900, 6.5cm. high.
$370 £190

Galle cameo glass stemmed honeycomb cup, 11.75cm. high, circa 1900.
$1,020 £550

GLASS DISHES

A Lalique glass circular dish with groups of birds in relief, 8½in. diam. $97 £48

A Galle cameo glass dish, 29cm. wide, circa 1904. $405 £200

Lalique frosted glass dish, 45.25cm. wide, 1920's. $435 £220

A high quality pate de cristal dish by Argy Rousseau. $455 £230

Glass centrepiece by Rene Lalique, circa 1925, 32cm. long. $505 £250

One of a set of four Lalique side plates, circa 1925. $505 £250

Galle glass dish carved as a shell, 1890's, 34cm. long. $588 £300

Daum cameo glass dish, 14.5cm. wide, circa 1900. $590 £320

Daum cameo glass dish and cover, circa 1900, 9.5cm. $630 £340

Large Lalique frosted
glass figure of a pigeon,
14.5cm. high, 1930's.
$775 £420

Lalique opalescent glass
figure of 'Suzanne au
Bain', 22.75cm. high,
1920's. $850 £460

A sea green and yel-
low pate de verre
figure of Loie Fuller
signed A. Walter
Nancy, 20.5cm. high.
$970 £480

Galle faience cat,
13in. high, 1880's,
signed.
$935 £520

Walter pate de verre figure
of a pike, 1920's, 53.25cm.
long. $1,350 £700

Pate de verre chameleon
paperweight by H. Berge
in deep green glass,
1910, 8.6cm. high.
$1,400 £700

20th century Lalique
glass figure of a kneel-
ing woman, 21cm.
high. $1,780 £900

Lalique glass figure
of a cockerel, 1930's,
19.5cm. high.
$2,375 £1,200

Pair of figures by
Lalique in frosted
glass, 56cm. high.
$5,720 £2,860

GLASS INKSTANDS

A Lalique amber glass inkwell and cover, 1920's, 15.75cm. diam.
$520 £280

Art Nouveau glass inkstand.
$850 £420

A rare Tiffany inkwell.
$1,820 £900

JUGS

A Lalique clear glass jug, the handle moulded with berries and foliage, 21cm. high.
$75 £36

Galle carved glass pitcher in smoked glass, 1890's, 15.5cm.
$850 £460

Silver mounted mauve glass claret jug by Elkington & Co., Birmingham 1897, 14in. high. $900 £500

A French cameo glass claret jug by Daum, 12½in. high.$1,515 £750

Cameo glass claret jug by Webb.
$1,560 £780

Silver mounted green glass decanter by the Guild of Handicrafts Ltd., 1901, 20.5cm. high. $3,335 £1,650

A modernist cocktail service, consisting of a decanter and six glasses, circa 1930. $180 £90

Modernist glass liqueur set with tray, 1930's. $235 £120

Attractive WMF silvered metal liqueur set, circa 1900, 37.5cm. high. $290 £150

Etched liqueur service in glass, 1930's. $380 £200

Rare glass tableware service in the Duncan pattern, by Rene Lalique, circa 1935. $4,950 £2,525

One of a set of six
black and white
glass buttons.
$7 £3.50

A Daum match-holder
of rectangular form, the
pale blue frosted glass
body enamelled with an
Alpine scene, 4cm. high.
$100 £50

Art Deco dressing
table set, circa
1930. $205 £100

Lalique glass
decanter, 12in.
high. $485 £240

Coffee and cream
glass centrepiece by
Webb, 10¼in. diam.
$525 £260

Daum pate de verre
paperweight, 13cm.
long, 1920's.
$630 £340

Unusual Galle enamel-
led glass pot pourri
jar, 30cm. high, circa
1890. $1,075 £580

Lalique glass bracket
shelf, 1930's, 26.25cm.
wide. $2,375 £1,200

Pair of Walter pate
de verre bookends,
1920's, 17cm. high.
$2,940 £1,500

Art Deco coloured
glass scent bottle.
        $24 £12

Glass perfume
bottle, circa
1920. $30 £15

Guerlain 'Mitsouko'
glass bottle and stop-
per. $40 £20

An opaline scent
bottle, circa
1880, 8½in. high.
    $50 £25

An Art Deco pink
tinted, cut glass
scent bottle.
        $57 £28

Moulded glass perfume
bottle and stopper,
1920's, 13cm. high.
            $55 £30

Black glass perfume
bottle with atomiser,
9.8cm. high.$55 £30

Delvaux enamelled
bottle and stopper,
1920's, 11.25cm.
high. $125 £65

Decorated clear glass
perfume bottle and
stopper, 13.75cm. high.
        $150 £80

GLASS
PERFUME BOTTLES

Moulded glass perfume
bottle and stopper of
triangular form, 1920's.
$160 £85

Moulded glass per-
fume bottle and
stopper, 12cm. high,
1920's. $190 £100

Decorated glass
atomiser, 10.5cm.
high, circa 1920.
$190 £100

Modernist glass bottle
and stopper, circa 1930,
26cm. high. $245 £130

Scent bottle cum
vinaigrette, Chester,
1913. $400 £210

Daum scent bottle
and stopper, 5in.
high, signed.
$470 £260

Webb cameo silver
mounted scent
flask, 7in. long.
$575 £320

Galle glass perfume
burner, 6½in. high.
$970 £480

A scent bottle
by Tiffany.
$1,210 £600

PLAQUES

Lalique plaque sold
with a similar piece.
$4,440 £2,200

An illuminated Lalique
glass plaque, carved
with a naked archer,
4in. diam. $960 £480

Rare Lalique panel
initialled L'oiseau
Du Feu, moulded in
relief, 17in. high.
$4,180 £2,090

Art glass plaque
by George
Woodall.
$8,485 £4,200

POTS

Fine bronze mounted
pate de verre plaque
of Isadora Duncan,
17½in. high.
$8,250 £4,435

Cameo glass plaque
by George Woodall,
circa 1885.
$23,230 £11,500

Lithyalin pounce-
pot with pewter
mount, 2¾in. high.
$305 £170

Silver mounted cameo
and applied glass pot
by Galle. $550 £275

Daum etched and
applied cameo glass
pot and cover, 12.5cm.
high, circa 1910.
$555 £300

Slim Art Nouveau vase in pale blue glass. $16 £8

Iridescent green blue vase with teardrop decoration. $18 £9

Three-handled Art Nouveau glass vase in green. $22 £11

Edwardian ruby glass vase in a plated mount, 9in. high. $30 £15

Late 19th century iridescent vase with applied decoration, 5½in. high. $30 £15

Late 19th century green and white glass vase, 10in. high. $36 £18

German clear glass vase in a silver plated pewter case by Crivit. $36 £18

Dark green Art Nouveau rippled glass vase in a brass case with lily pad design. $53 £26

Art Nouveau vase decorated with snails in fiery orange and silver blue. $65 £32

Moser iridescent glass
vase in graded mul-
berry tinged with
pink. $70 £35

Art Nouveau glass vase
in pale lime green with
brown bullrushes ris-
ing from the base.
            $100 £50

Signed Sabino vase,
circa 1920, with
fish motif, 8in.
high. $110 £55

Legras etched and in-
ternally decorated
glass vase, 1920's,
31.5cm. high.
            $115 £60

Pair of Art Nouveau
blue cameo vases,
10in. high.
            $130 £65

Legras etched and in-
ternally decorated
glass vase, 39cm. high,
1920's. $140 £75

Art Nouveau glass
vase with metal
mounts.$170 £85

Clutha glass vase in
olive green with
white and blue stri-
ations, circa 1895.
            $180 £90

A Legras cameo glass
vase of quatrefoil
shape, 13cm. high.
            $200 £100

GLASS VASES

One of a pair of Georg Adam Scheid plique-a-jour vases, 13.75cm. high, circa 1900.
$280 £150

Orrefors engraved glass vase, 18.75cm. high, 1940's, sold with another. $280 £150

De Vez cameo glass landscape vase, circa 1900-1910, 22.25cm. high.
$335 £180

A gilt and enamelled Marcel Goupy vase, 24.5cm. high, 1920's.
$335 £180

Durand blue iridescent glass vase, 18.8cm. high, circa 1910. $350 £190

Le verre Francais cameo glass vase, 1920's, 47.5cm. high. $380 £200

Le verre Francais-Charder cameo glass vase, 1920's, 35cm. high.
$420 £220

An Orrefors glass vase, by Vicke Lindstrand, circa 1930, 3½in. high. $505 £250

Degue overlaid and etched glass vase, 1920's, 40.5cm. high.
$530 £280

Argy Rousseau pate
de cristal vase,
14.75cm. high,
1920's. $850 £460

Angular pate de cris-
tal vase by Gabriel
Argy Rousseau, cast
in emerald green mar-
bled glass, 1925.
$970 £480

Burgun and Schwerer
wheel carved vase in
bluebell purple and
gilt. $970 £480

A good, heavy Art
Deco glass vase, by
Andre Thuret,
1930.
$1,010 £500

A pate de cristal vase
by Francois Emile
Decorchemont, circa
1927. $1,090 £540

Good piece of Art
Nouveau glass-
ware. $1,140 £600

Pate de verre small
oviform vase,
3¼in. diameter.
$1,350 £750

Argy Rousseau pate
de verre vase,
12¼in. high.
$5,500 £2,750

Pate de cristal vase by
Francois Decorchemont
in deep blue glass,
25.5cm. high, circa
1910. $6,665 £3,300

73

GLASS
DAUM VASES

Daum enamelled glass vase, 1920's, 18.5cm. high. $165 £90

Daum etched and enamelled glass vase, circa 1900, 8cm. high. $295 £160

Daum etched glass vase, circa 1900, 12.25cm. high. $315 £170

Carved cameo glass vase by Daum, 37cm. high, circa 1900. $590 £320

Daum cameo glass vase, circa 1900, 16.5cm. high. $705 £380

Daum etched and wheel carved cameo glass vase, 26.5cm. high, circa 1900. $835 £450

Daum etched, carved and enamelled glass vase, circa 1900, 13.5cm. high. $925 £500

Daum cameo glass vase of teardrop form, 30.25cm. high, circa 1900. $925 £500

A deep etched glass vase by Daum, circa 1925. $1,110 £550

GALLE VASES

GLASS

Miniature Galle cameo glass vase, 5.25cm. high, circa 1900, with ribbed stem. $185 £100

Small Galle cameo glass vase, 7.75cm. high, circa 1900. $280 £150

Small Galle cameo glass vase, circa 1900, 8.5cm. high. $295 £160

Galle cameo glass vase, circa 1904, 19.5cm. high. $295 £160

Galle cameo glass vase, after 1904, 17.5cm. high. $295 £160

Galle cameo glass landscape vase, circa 1900, 11.75cm. high. $405 £220

Galle cameo glass vase with ovoid body, 12cm. high, circa 1904. $445 £240

Galle cameo glass vase, circa 1900, 19.5cm. high. $445 £240

Galle cameo glass mountainscape vase, 12cm. high, circa 1900. $480 £260

Galle cameo glass vase with irregular rim, circa 1900, 13.25cm. high.
$480 £260

A Galle cameo glass vase of tall slender baluster form, the grey, orange body overlaid in crimson, 35cm. high.
$555 £275

Galle cameo glass vase, circa 1900, 16.5cm. high. $665 £360

Galle cameo glass landscape vase, 21.5cm. high, circa 1900.
$665 £360

Galle cameo glass vase, 13.75cm. high, circa 1900. $705 £380

Galle etched and carved glass vase, 14.75cm. high, 1890's.
$705 £380

Large Galle glass vase of ovoid form, 50cm. high, circa 1904.
$775 £420

Galle cameo glass vase and stopper, circa 1900, 20.5cm. high.
$815 £440

Galle cameo glass vase, 46.5cm. high, after 1904. $815 £440

Galle cameo glass vase,
25.5cm. high, circa
1900. $850 £460

Galle cameo glass vase,
with inverted rim,
20.75cm. high, circa
1900. $890 £480

Galle cameo glass
vase, overlaid in
brown, 43.5cm.
high.$970 £480

Galle etched and carved
cameo glass vase,
19.5cm. high, circa
1900. $890 £480

Galle boat-shaped cameo
glass vase, 19cm. wide,
circa 1900. $925 £500

Galle carved glass
vase, 28cm. high,
1890's.$960 £520

Large Galle glass vase,
circa 1900, 50.75cm.
high. $1,075 £580

Galle cameo glass vase,
circa 1900, 22cm. high,
with boat-shaped rim.
$1,200 £650

Galle cameo glass vase
in amber, 49cm. high,
circa 1900.
$1,295 £700

GLASS
GALLE VASES

Mounted Galle cameo
glass vase, circa 1890's,
7.75cm. high.
$1,480 £800

Large Galle landscape
cameo glass vase,
44.25cm. high, circa
1900. $1,570 £850

Good etched and
carved Galle cameo
glass vase, 18.25cm.
high.$2,035 £1,100

Good Galle cameo
glass vase, 19.5cm.
high, circa 1900.
$2,405 £1,300

Good Galle cameo glass
vase, 19.5cm. high, circa
1900. $2,405 £1,300

A fine and rare mar-
quetry vase by Emile
Galle, made in 1900.
$5,555 £2,750

Glass vase by Emile
Galle, with an applied
decoration of a glass
rose, around 1900.
$9,290 £4,600

Glass vase by Emile
Galle, 11¾in. high.
$36,820 £19,275

Internally decorated, carved and applied glass vase
by Emile Galle, 1900,
23.2cm. high.
$39,600 £22,000

Lalique frosted glass
vase, 1930's, 17.75cm.
high. $120 £65

Bulbous Lalique frosted
glass vase, 25.5cm. high,
1920's. $130 £70

Lalique frosted glass
vase, 1930's, 15.5cm.
high. $150 £80

Lalique frosted glass
vase, 1930's, 15.25cm.
high. $155 £85

Mid 20th century Lalique
frosted glass vase, 16.75cm.
high. $155 £85

Lalique frosted glass
vase, 17.5cm. high,
1930's. $165 £90

Lalique frosted glass
vase, circa 1920,
21.25cm. high.
            $175 £95

Lalique opalescent glass
vase, 22.75cm. high,
1920's. $175 £95

Lalique enamelled
glass vase, 12.25cm.
high, 1920's.
            $185 £100

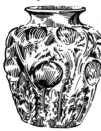

Lalique frosted glass vase, 1930's, 21.25cm. high. $185 £100

Mid 20th century Lalique frosted glass vase, 19.5cm. high. $205 £110

Squat Lalique frosted glass vase, 17.75cm. high, 1930's. $205 £110

Lalique opalescent glass vase, 18cm. high, 1930's. $220 £120

Lalique smoked glass vase, 11.5cm. high, 1920's, of flattened spherical body. $260 £140

Lalique opalescent glass vase, 1930's, 22cm. high. $295 £160

Heavy Lalique frosted glass vase, 1930's, 25.5cm. high. $335 £180

Lalique opalescent glass vase, 22.5cm. high, 1920's. $370 £200

Lalique oviform vase, 9½in. high. $430 £240

Heavy Lalique cylindrical glass vase, 22.5cm. high, 1920's.
$445 £240

Spherical Lalique frosted glass vase, 25.5cm. high, 1920's.
$480 £260

Lalique frosted glass vase, 15cm., 1920's.
$705 £380

Bulbous Lalique glass vase, 24.75cm. high, 1920's. $740 £400

Lalique globular vase, 10in. diam. $755 £420

A superb vase by Rene Lalique, circa 1925.
$1,160 £575

Good Lalique 'grasshopper' vase, 27cm. high, 1920's.
$1,760 £950

Lalique frosted glass vase, 24.75cm. high, 1920's. $2,590 £1,400

A Lalique vase, with a border of Bacchantes. $4,040 £2,000

81

GLASS
LOETZ VASES

Loetz iridescent glass vase, circa 1900, 12.5cm. high.
$220 £120

Loetz iridescent glass vase, 14.25cm. high, circa 1900.
$220 £120

Loetz iridescent vase, circa 1900, 27.5cm. high.
$260 £140

Loetz iridescent glass vase, 18.5cm. high, circa 1900.$275 £150

I oetz iridescent glass vase, circa 1900, 15cm. high.
$295 £160

Loetz iridescent glass vase, circa 1900, 17.25cm. high.
$315 £170

Loetz iridescent glass vase, 12.5cm. high, circa 1900.$370 £200

Loetz iridescent glass vase, circa 1900, 17cm. high.
$405 £220

Loetz iridescent glass vase, circa 1900, 21.25cm. high.
$445 £240

Loetz iridescent glass
vase, circa 1900,
7.75cm. high.
$445 £240

Loetz iridescent glass
vase, 15.75cm. high,
circa 1900.
$555 £300

Good Loetz iridescent
glass vase, 17.5cm.
high, circa 1900.
$590 £320

Good Loetz iridescent
vase, 18.5cm. high,
circa 1900.$630 £340

A Loetz glass bottle
vase with a blue
base decorated with
flame designs.
$910 £450

Loetz baluster iridescent
glass vase, circa 1900,
32.5cm. high.$890 £480

Good Loetz iridescent
glass vase, circa 1900,
12.5cm. high.
$925 £500

Loetz iridescent glass vase,
circa 1900, 26.25cm. high.
$960 £520

Loetz iridescent glass
vase, circa 1900, 20cm.
high. $1,015 £550

GLASS
TIFFANY VASES

Tiffany iridescent glass vase, 9.5cm. high, 1912.
$260 £140

Tiffany peacock lily-pad vase, 1900.
$555 £275

Tiffany Favrile iridescent millifiori oviform vase, 6in. high.$1,080 £600

A Tiffany Cypriot vase.
$1,335 £660

Tiffany vase, richly feathered in green, gold and peacock, iridescent shades, 1900.
$1,695 £840

Tiffany iridescent glass solifleur vase, 35.25cm. high, 1907.
$2,035 £1,100

Tiffany flower vase of milky tone, 44cm. high. $2,700 £1,350

Gold and yellow iridescent vase by Louis C. Tiffany, 38cm. high, circa 1900.
$4,445 £2,200

A rare Jack-in-the Pulpit Tiffany peacock iridescent glass vase, 1900.
$8,080 £4,000

WEBB VASES

GLASS

A Webb glass cameo vase, 9in. high. $505 £250

A fine white and blue Webb cameo vase.
$910 £450

A superb vase by Thomas Webb.
$2,240 £1,110

WINDOWS

Early 20th century stained glass window depicting a peacock, 22in. high. $70 £35

Large, 20th century, stained glass window depicting a ship in full sail. $80 £40

'Birds and Fishes' window design by Webb.
$810 £400

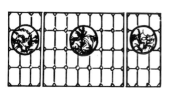

A triptych stained glass thistle window by Tiffany, circa 1904, 36in. wide.
$2,020 £1,000

A triptych stained glass landscape window, circa 1905. $3,030 £1,500

HAIR COMBS

Art Nouveau
tortoiseshell
hair comb.
$30 £15

Two pronged comb
made of stained
horn. $70 £35

Art Nouveau
comb of pale
coloured horn.
$80 £40

English tortoise-
shell comb with
gold design set
with turquoises.
$325 £160

English tortoiseshell
comb with flowing
gold design set with
turquoises.
$325 £160

One of a pair of
French hair combs
of horn adorned
with silver lilies.
$555 £275

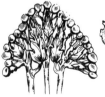

Good carved horn,
enamel and moon-
stone hair comb,
circa 1900, 13.1cm.
wide. $960 £520

Carved horn, gold, enamel
and mother-of-pearl hair
ornament by Lalique,
circa 1900, 17.5cm. wide.
$2,590 £1,400

Art Nouveau hair orna-
ment set with rose
diamonds and pearls.
$7,200 £4,000

86

Ivory and silver pepper-
mill in the form of a
milk churn, 1897.
$115 £60

Pair of German ivory
figures of children on
circular plinths, 19cm.
high. $305 £150

Small Preiss carved
ivory figure, circa
1920, 15cm. high.
$345 £175

Preiss ivory and onyx group
depicting woodland friends,
5½in. high, signed, circa
1930. $405 £200

Walther carved ivory
figure of a young girl,
8.75cm. high, 1930's.
$415 £225

Preiss carved ivory
figure of a little girl,
15.25cm. high,
1920's. $480 £260

Preiss carved ivory
figure of a little boy,
14.75cm. high, 1930's.
$480 £260

Model of a sea nymph
rising from the waves.
$605 £300

Carved ivory female
head by Julien Dillens,
55cm. high, circa 1900.
$2,605 £1,400

87

Heart-shaped silver and enamel brooch, circa 1900, 3.25cm. wide. $120 £65

Austrian pendant and matching earring set, circa 1910. $120 £65

Enamel pendant, circa 1900, 7cm. long. $155 £85

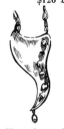

Gold brooch set with a green-beige cabochon, circa 1900, 3.5cm. wide. $175 £95

Unusual enamelled pendant on silver coloured metal, 5cm. long, circa 1905. $220 £120

Gold and opal brooch, 3.25cm., circa 1900. $220 £120

Gold, pearl and black opal brooch, circa 1900, 3cm. wide. $280 £150

A pair of silver and enamel cufflinks, 2.25cm. high, circa 1900. $280 £150

Charles Horner silver and enamel brooch, 2.75cm. wide, Chester, 1903. $295 £160

Art Nouveau gold
and enamel fairy
pendant.$355 £175

Dunand eggshell lac-
quer pendant panel,
13.8cm. long.
$543 £280

Attractive William Hutton
& Sons Ltd., silver and enamel belt, London, 1904.
$630 £340

Liberty & Co. gold,
pearl and mother-of-
pearl necklace, circa
1900-05.$665 £360

An Art Deco diamond
and sapphire brooch
with a central triangu-
lar cut diamond.
$1,515 £750

Lalique gold and enamel
brooch, 3.4cm. wide,
circa 1900.$2,405 £1,300

Gold, carved chrysoprase,
baroque pearl and diamond
Art Nouveau brooch, 5cm.,
circa 1900. $2,775 £1,500

Corsage ornament by
Georges Fouquet.
$46,115 £23,530

Pendant by Alphonse
Mucha and Georges
Fouquet.
$53,290 £26,380

LAMPS

Elegant bronze Art Nouveau lamp, 15in. high. $160 £80

Lamp as a lady dressed in black and silver with ivorine face and hands, 10in. high, 1920's. $200 £100

Art Deco bronze table lamp, French, circa 1925, 38cm. high. $310 £160

Gilt metal Art Deco lamp, circa 1920. $400 £210

Art Deco bronze lamp, 1930's, 52.75cm. high. $515 £260

Attractive Boilot bronze table lamp, circa 1900, 39.5cm. high. $775 £400

Spelter lamp, 16in. high, 1920's, fitted for electricity. $785 £400

Favrile glass and gilt bronze desk lamp by Tiffany, 9¼in. high. $770 £415

Gilt metal mounted stoneware lamp base by Doulton, 22¼in. high, dated 1882. $925 £500

Small etched glass table lamp attributed to Daum, 33.75cm. high, circa 1900. $925 £500

Lalique lamp in frosted glass, 1920's, 10½in. high. $1,050 £520

Tiffany studios bronze lamp base, circa 1910, 57.5cm. high. $1,225 £620

Galle glass table lamp, signed, about 1900, 35cm. high. $1,295 £640

One of a pair of iridescent Favrile glass candle lamps, by Tiffany, 14in. high. $1,265 £680

Gilt bronze and Favrile glass three-light lily table lamp by Tiffany, 13in. high. $1,320 £710

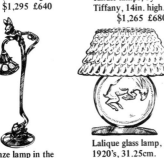

Bronze lamp in the style of Gurschner. $1,620 £900

Lalique glass lamp, 1920's, 31.25cm. high. $1,940 £1,000

Daum etched and enamelled glass table lamp, 37.35cm. high, circa 1900. $1,850 £1,000

LAMPS

Early 20th century silver plated table lamp in the Art Nouveau style, 38in high. $2,120 £1,050

Bronze and ivory two-light table lamp by Preiss, 26in. high.
$2,135 £1,100

A superb etched and enamelled glass table lamp.
$2,220 £1,100

Daum cameo glass lamp, circa 1900, 44.5cm. high.
$2,405 £1,300

Tiffany studios bronze table lamp with leaded glass shade, circa 1900, 63.25cm. high. $2,770 £1,400

German or Austrian Art Nouveau lamp, 69cm. high. $2,510 £1,300

Tiffany studio bronze table lamp, 34.5cm. high, 1910-20.
$2,775 £1,500

A bronze and shell lamp by Gurschner.
$4,040 £2,000

Art Nouveau leaded glass and bronze table lamp, circa 1910, 64.5cm. high.
$3,880 £2,000

92

Galle cameo glass
table lamp.
$5,040 £2,800

Early Favrile glass and
silvered bronze kerosene
student lamp by Tiffany,
24in. high.$5,500 £2,955

Tiffany studio bronze
table lamp, circa 1900,
63cm. high.
$5,550 £3,000

Poppy leaded glass and
gilt bronze table lamp
by Tiffany, 25½in.
high. $10,450 £5,620

Galle cameo glass lamp,
circa 1900, 34.25cm.
high. $9,800 £5,000

Rare blown and carved
glass bronze mounted
table lamp, by Emile
Galle, circa 1900, 42cm.
high. $18,500 £10,000

Poppy leaded glass
and bronze table lamp
by Tiffany, 27¼in.
high. $19,800 £10,205

Tiffany studio
wisteria lamp.
$32,320 £16,000

Daum glass lamp
carved with marine
motifs.
$32,145 £16,400

20th century painted
glass hanging shade.
$20 £10

Czechoslovakian
peach hanging
chandelier, 1920.
$150 £75

Art Deco wrought iron
and Schneider glass
chandelier, 1930's,
67cm. wide.$390 £200

Art Nouveau brass
chandelier, circa
1900. $185 £95

Highly coloured Bel-
gian chandelier by
Muller, 61cm. high.
$505 £250

Lalique glass multi-
ple panel hanging
shade, 1920's,
49cm. diameter.
$590 £300

Favrile glass and
bronze chandelier
by Tiffany Studios,
20in. high.
$990 £510

Glass chandelier by
Rene Lalique, 12in.
diameter.
$1,200 £605

Fine glass ceiling fix-
ture by Rene Lalique,
circa 1925, 10¾in.
diam. $2,000 £1,010

Iridescent Favrile glass
chandelier by Tiffany,
shade 14in. high.
$2,420 £1,245

Double overlay glass
chandelier by Daum
Freres, 15½in. diam.
$2,500 £1,260

Gilt bronze and Favrile
glass ceiling fixture by
Tiffany, 17in. high.
$3,000 £1,515

Good Wiener Werkstatte
electroplated metal and
glass ceiling light, circa
1905, 26cm. high.
$3,685 £1,900

Tiffany pendant coloured
glass light shade, 28in.
diam. $4,240 £2,100

Rare green glass and
bronze chandelier by
Tiffany, 46in. high.
$12,000 £6,060

Favrile glass turtle-
back and leaded
glass chandelier by
Tiffany, 34½in. high.
$12,000 £6,060

Yellow rose bush leaded
glass hanging lamp by
Tiffany, 24¾in. diam.
$17,600 £9,460

A rare calamander
leaded glass chande-
lier by Tiffany, 48in.
high.
$30,000 £15,150

95

One of a pair of
stylised chromed
metal standard
lamps, 1930's,
179.5cm. high.
$230 £120

1930's standard
lamp, with white
glass shade,
188cm. high.
$195 £100

Art Deco wrought
iron standard
lamp, 167cm.
high, circa 1925.
$295 £160

Leaded glass and
bronze bridge
floor lamp by
Tiffany, 54½in.
high. $880 £475

Bronze and Fav-
rile glass linen
fold floor lamp
by Tiffany,
55in. high.
$1,210 £650

Wrought iron and
glass floor lamp,
circa 1945,
64½in. high.
$2,420 £1,245

Favrile glass and
bronze bridge
floor lamp by
Tiffany, 55½in.
high.
$2,640 £1,420

Gilt bronze and
Favrile glass
twelve-light lily
floor lamp by
Tiffany, 55¼in.
high.
$8,800 £4,730

Pugi white marble figure, circa 1925, 45.5cm. high.
$295 £150

Russian or French blue marble vase, circa 1930, 8in. high.
$405 £200

Marble mandarin duck, 1920's, 17.5cm. high.
$590 £300

Marble portrait bust of Helen Boucher, 42cm. high, circa 1930. $605 £300

MISCELLANEOUS

Marble carving of Loie Fuller by T. Riviere.
$1,415 £700

A superb plaster figure, in relief, 73½in. high.
$1,515 £750

English/American wicker-work pram, 4ft.4in. long, 1930's. $48 £25

A pair of polished steel firedogs of the Art Nouveau period, design by Ernest Gimson, and made by Alfred Bucknell, circa 1910. $1,715 £850

Attractive Templeton's carpet, by Charles Rennie Mackintosh, circa 1910, 455cm. x 358cm.
$2,405 £1,300

97

MIRRORS

Large Art Deco
mirror frame,
early 1920's.
$115 £60

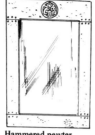

Hammered pewter
mirror with enamel
blue decoration.
$240 £120

WMF silvered metal
mirror frame, circa
1910, 40.75cm.
high. $235 £120

Stylish Hagenauer
chromed metal
hand mirror, 1920's,
21.5cm. high.$255 £130

Unusual copper overman-
tel mirror, circa 1900,
62in. long. $280 £150

Rubin bronze Art
Nouveau hand mir-
ror, 27.75cm. long,
circa 1900.
$350 £190

Silver Art Nouveau
photograph frame by
J. & A. Zimmerman,
29cm. high, Birming-
ham, 1903.$375 £190

Sue and Mare Art
Deco gilt bronze
mirror frame, 1923,
25.6cm. high.
$395 £200

Liberty & Co. silver
and enamel frame,
Birmingham, 1910,
27cm. high.
$435 £220

Austrian Art Nouveau bronze mirror, 35.5cm. high, circa 1900.
$465 £240

Guernardeau patinated metal Art Nouveau mirror frame, circa 1900, 41.5cm. high. $465 £250

Silver and enamel frame by Wm. Hutton & Sons Ltd., London, 1903, 19.75cm. high. $660 £340

Pewter Art Nouveau mirror frame, 49.5cm. high, German, circa 1900. $1,190 £600

Good Lalique glass hand mirror, 1920's, 29.75cm. high. $1,175 £600

One of two Liberty & Co. silver frames, Birmingham, 1905, 19.25cm. high.
$1,260 £650

Rosewood and mahogany mirror by Louis Majorelle, 67in. high.
$3,000 £1,515

Italian Art Nouveau mirror with carved pearwood frame, 92½in. high.
$4,620 £2,390

Silver and enamel mirror frame by Liberty & Co., 18¾in. high.
$5,335 £2,640

PEWTER

Early 20th century pewter napkin ring. $4 £2

Art Nouveau pewter sugar basin with floral decoration. $30 £15

Early 20th century Art Nouveau pewter vase, 5in. high. $44 £22

Pewter Art Nouveau lady leaning over lily pond, 7in. high. $70 £35

Early 20th century pewter letter rack decorated with coloured stones, 14in. wide. $70 £35

Pewter fruit tazza, about 1905, 10½in. high. $72 £40

Polished pewter water jug with cane handle by Liberty & Co., circa 1905. $76 £42

Liberty & Co. pewter butter dish and knife in 'Tudric' style, after 1903, 17.75cm. long. $155 £80

Gilbert Parks pewter charger, 20¼in. diam., dated 1899. $185 £100

Kayserzinn pewter jug, circa 1905, 26.75cm. high.
$245 £125

Silvered metal plaque 'The Spirit of Christ-mas', by John G. Hardy, circa 1895, 41cm. long.
$240 £130

Liberty & Co. 'Tudric' pewter and enamel biscuit box and cover, 14cm. high, after 1903. $295 £150

Large Moreau silvered pewter tray, 45cm. wide, circa 1900.
$295 £150

Liberty & Co. 'Tudric' pewter stand with glass liner, circa 1905, 16.5cm. high.
$295 £150

One of a pair of Liberty & Co. 'Tudric' pewter and enamel candlesticks, circa 1905, 16cm. high.
$345 £175

Liberty & Co. 'Tudric' pewter bowl with glass liner, circa 1905, 10.25cm. high.
$345 £175

Large metal tazza, 44cm. high, WMF marks, 1900-1910.
$335 £180

Large WMF Art Nouveau pewter tureen and cover, circa 1900, 48cm. high.
$390 £200

PEWTER

WMF silvered metal and glass tazza, circa 1900, 36.25cm. high. $480 £260

Liberty & Co. six-piece pewter tea and coffee service. $525 £260

Unusual Liberty & Co. 'Tudric' pewter mounted green glass jug, after 1903. $485 £260

Large WMF pewter jardiniere, 32.5cm. wide, circa 1900. $595 £300

WMF pewter Art Nouveau garniture, circa 1900. $560 £300

WMF pewter candlestick, 26.25cm. high, circa 1900.$675 £340

WMF pewter mounted green glass decanter, circa 1900, 38.5cm. high. $710 £360

A pair of Art Nouveau pewter candlesticks, 16½in. high. $725 £360

Edelzinn pewter jug, circa 1901, 33.5cm. high. $2,775 £1,500

102

English Celestian radio speaker in mahogany cabinet. $44 £22

An English Amplion radio speaker in domed wooden case. $69 £34

A rare American National microphone dancer, 1ft.1in. high, circa 1935. $255 £125

Rare American radio in the form of a Coca-Cola bottle, 24in. high, circa 1930. $365 £180

Early 20th century walnut and ebony cabinet, designed by Edward Barnsley, designed to house a gramophone and records. $455 £225

Operaphone gramophone, circa 1925-30, 3ft. high. $505 £280

Good Edison Amberola VIII phonograph, American, circa 1913. $565 £300

Wurlitzer Simplex jukebox, 1936, with twelve records. $1,440 £800

Wurlitzer jukebox with twenty-four records. $3,840 £1,900

SILVER
BISCUIT BARRELS

Cut glass biscuit box of Art Nouveau design with a plated stand and cover.
$40 £20

Circular biscuit barrel, 5½in. high, London, 1931, 17oz. 6dwt.
$200 £110

Art Nouveau lantern style biscuitiere with glass liner, 1900.
$2,970 £1,650

BOWLS

William Hutton & Sons Ltd. silver bowl, London, 1909, 20.5cm. diam.
$290 £150

Large Maurel Art Nouveau patinated metal jardiniere, circa 1900, 29cm. high.
$635 £320

A Guild of Handicrafts silver and green enamel bowl by Charles Robert Ashbee, 11.5cm. high.
$1,615 £800

Lidded silver rose bowl by Omar Ramsden.
$2,470 £1,300

Enamelled silver kovsch by Carl Faberge, circa 1910, 2½in. long.
$2,420 £1,300

Circular silver rose bowl by Omar Ramsden, 1935, 70oz. 18dwt., 11¾in. wide.
$3,535 £1,750

Silver and enamel buckle, 4.6cm. diameter, English, circa 1900. $100 £55

Art Nouveau belt buckle, 7.75cm. wide, probably American, circa 1900.
$140 £75

W. H. Haseler & Sons silver and enamel belt buckle, Birmingham, 1907, 9.5cm. high. $175 £95

Liberty & Co. silver belt buckle, 7.25cm. wide, Birmingham, 1900. $205 £110

Liberty & Co. silver belt buckle, 11cm. wide, Birmingham, 1902. $315 £170

A Liberty silver and enamel buckle in the manner of Jessie M. King, Birmingham, 1908. $355 £175

French Art Nouveau belt buckle, 7.5cm. wide, circa 1900, gilt teeth. $405 £220

Liberty & Co. silver and enamel belt buckle, Birmingham, 1906, 8.75cm. wide. $890 £480

SILVER CANDLESTICKS

One of a pair of Liberty & Co. 'Cymric' silver candlesticks, Birmingham, 1904, 14.75cm. high.
$335 £180

One of two Cooper Bros. & Sons Ltd. silver candlesticks, 19cm. high, 1903.
$505 £260

One of a pair of James Dixon & Sons large silver candlesticks, Sheffield, 1918, 30.5cm. high. $695 £350

Fine Georg Jensen silver three-branched candelabrum, circa 1930, 15¾in. high.
$2,200 £1,122

CENTREPIECES

One of a pair of Georg Jensen silver candlesticks, circa 1920, 5½in. high. $1,750 £920

Stylish German six-light candelabrum, circa 1910, 57cm. high, in silver coloured metal.
$5,150 £2,600

Georg Jensen silver centrepiece, 10¼in. diam. $1,430 £745

One of a pair of Georg Jensen centrepieces, circa 1927, 7¾in. diam.
$2,750 £1,445

Large Jensen silver coupe, London, 1922, 19.75cm. high. $2,940 £1,500

106

1930's hand car-
ved aluminium
cigarette case.
$40 £20

German cigarette
case, circa 1910,
10.5cm. long.
$100 £52

Silver Art Nou-
veau cigarette
case, Birmingham,
1905, 9cm. high.
$195 £100

Silver and enamel
cigarette case, 8cm.
wide, Glasgow,
1926. $198 £100

Eggshell lacquer
cigarette case,
1920's, 8.5cm.
high.$345 £175

Silver and eggshell
lacquer cigarette
case, 8.2cm. wide,
1926. $395 £200

Silver and enamel
cigarette case,
1925, 8.4cm. wide.
$395 £200

Eggshell lacquer
modernist ciga-
rette case, late
1920's, 11.6cm.
wide. $395 £200

Eggshell lacquer
modernist ciga-
rette case, 11.6cm.
wide, late 1920's.
$990 £500

107

SILVER CIGARETTE BOXES

German silvered metal box, circa 1905, 16cm. wide. $480 £260

Art Nouveau silver cigarette box by Omar Ramsden and Alwyn Carr, 5¾in. long. $830 £410

Unusual enamelled silver box in the form of an outsize matchbox, London, 1905. $850 £420

COCKTAIL SHAKERS

A plated cocktail shaker. $16 £8

A plated cocktail set of six pieces on a wooden stand. $24 £12

Georg Jensen silver cocktail shaker, circa 1927, 12¼in. high. $600 £305

CONDIMENTS

Gallia cruet set, 8cm. high, in silvered metal, 1920's. $155 £85

Art Nouveau silver mustard pot with blue glass liner. $200 £100

A pair of Handicrafts Ltd. pepper casters, circa 1900, 6.5cm. high. $425 £220

Edwardian silver
double-handled
prize cup, 5oz.
5dwt. $30 £15

An Art Nouveau
cup by Gilbert
Marks.
$255 £125

One of a pair of sil-
ver stemmed cups,
Chester, 1905,
17.5cm. high.
$435 £220

William Hutton &
Sons Ltd., twin-
handled silver cup,
28cm. high, London,
1902. $405 £220

Standing cup by
Omar Ramsden,
7¼in. high, Lon-
don, 1938, 24oz.
15dwt. $485 £240

W. C. Connell sil-
ver gilt two-han-
dled cup, 1907,
21.5cm. high.
$505 £260

A rare Nazi Luft-
waffe silver honour
goblet. $655 £325

Hammered silver cup
by C. R. Ashbee, Lon-
don, 1901.
$1,060 £525

Wm. Hutton & Sons Ltd.,
two-handled cup and
cover, Birmingham, 1903,
32cm. high. $2,220 £1,200

**SILVER
DISHES**

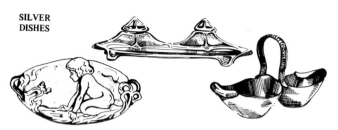

German Art Nouveau sil-
vered metal oval dish,
marked WMF, EP, 10in.
long. $50 £25

Art Nouveau electro-
plated dish, circa
1900, 33.75cm. wide.
          $120 £60

Hukin and Heath silver
sweetmeat dish, 14cm.
high, London, 1881.
          $240 £130

Austrian electroplated
dish, 17.5cm. high,
circa 1910-20.
          $295 £150

Small Jensen silver
footed dish, 5.25cm.
high, 1936.
          $280 £150

French Art Deco
electroplated dish
and cover, circa
1925, 17cm. wide.
          $295 £150

WMF silvered metal
dish, circa 1900,
17.5cm. high.
          $315 £160

WMF silvered metal Art
Nouveau dish, 47cm.
wide, circa 1900.
          $335 £170

WMF silvered metal
dish, 26.25cm. wide,
circa 1900.
          $395 £200

Circular dish by Omar Ramsden, London, 1930, 6in. diam., 6oz. 9dwt. **$505 £250**

Austrian lobed dish, 27cm. diameter, after 1922, on four ball feet. **$405 £220**

Attractive WMF silvered metal dish, 21cm. high, circa 1900. **$560 £300**

Small Wiener Werkstatte dish, circa 1910-20, 10cm. diameter.**$620 £320**

One of a pair of Georg Jensen covered sweetmeat dishes, circa 1920, 6in. high. **$825 £435**

One of three silver dessert dishes, 12¾in. and 11½in. wide, maker's mark A.R., London, 1903, 73oz. **$890 £440**

Guild of Handicrafts Ltd. silver dish with single loop handle, 19cm. wide, London, 1906. **$835 £450**

Good hand-hammered Wiener Werkstatte footed dish, 34.25cm. wide, circa 1910-20. **$2,850 £1,500**

Guild of Handicrafts Ltd. silver and enamel twin loop handle dish and cover, 29.5cm. wide, London, 1901. **$3,145 £1,700**

SILVER
FLATWARE

Pair of plated salad servers made in 1920's. $20 £10

Liberty & Co. 'Cymric' spoon in silver, Birmingham, 1902, 16cm. long.
                    $295 £150

Georg Jensen silver serving spoon and fork, circa 1920. $300 £150

Guild of Handicrafts Ltd. silver butter knife, circa 1900, 13.5cm. long.
                    $330 £170

Bubeniczek paper knife, silver coloured metal handle, Austrian, circa 1900, 32.75cm. long. $400 £200

One of a set of six 'Cymric' silver and enamel spoons by Liberty & Co., 1903. $605 £300

Liberty & Co. 'Cymric' silver and enamel spoon, 1901, 20.5cm. long.
                    $980 £500

Good set of twelve, Liberty & Co., silver and enamel spoons, Birmingham, 1904. $925 £500

Part of a seventy-eight piece Georg Jensen silver flatware service in the Cypress pattern, 1954. $1,500 £785

Forty-four pieces of table silver by Omar Ramsden, London, 1926-38, 54oz.8dwt. (excluding Knives).
$1,615 £800

Fine Georg Jensen silver flatware service, circa 1909. $3,500 £1,765

Georg Jensen silver flatware service in cactus pattern, ninety-four pieces.
$4,180 £2,190

INKSTANDS

Edwardian silver inkstand, on four ball feet with glass bottle, 4oz. 15dwt. $32 £16

Edwardian silver plated inkwell by Mappin & Webb, about 1910. $77 £38

Hammered inkwell of capstan form by O. Ramsden, London, 1920, 6in. diam. $360 £180

SILVER JUGS

Elkington silver plate cream jug, about 1890, 3½in. high.
$30 £15

Late 19th century silver hot water jug with an ebony handle, 9oz.
$60 £30

Silver ewer with 'electro texture' handgrip.
$180 £90

Liberty & Co. silver coffee pot, 24.5cm. high, circa 1900.
$330 £170

Silver plated glass claret jug by Christopher Dresser.
$365 £180

Victorian silver mounted clear glass lotus claret jug, 7¼in. high, by E. H. Stockwell, London, 1880.
$565 £280

Hukin & Heath Ltd. silver mounted claret jug, London, 1883, 21.5cm. high. $555 £300

Silver mounted claret jug made by James Powell & Son, London, 1904.
$910 £450

Silver wine jug by Christopher Dresser, circa 1885.
$1,010 £500

Silver gilt Art Deco box with enamel target design. $70 £35

Small Liberty & Co. silver and enamel vesta case, Birmingham, 1902, 4.75cm. high. $79 £40

Chromed metal mother-of-pearl and abalone 'super kid' perfume atomiser, 1920's, 5.2cm. high. $105 £55

Attractive Art Nouveau walking stick with silvered metal top, German, circa 1900. $105 £55

Stylish German silver mesh evening purse, circa 1910, 18cm. long. $117 £60

French Art Nouveau silver smoker's set, circa 1900. $180 £90

Cylindrical scent flask by Ramsden & Carr, 3½in. high, London, 1906. $210 £105

Good Kayserzinn meat dish and cover, 55cm. long, circa 1900. $230 £120

Hukin & Heath toast rack, 12cm., 1880's, on curved base. $280 £150

SILVER MISCELLANEOUS

Silver mounted glass jar and cover by W. C. Connell, London, 1901, 14.75cm. high.
$350 £190

French Art Nouveau cane handle, circa 1900. $380 £210

Bruder Frank kettle and stand, circa 1900, in silver coloured metal. $539 £275

One of twelve silver gilt menu holders, Birmingham, 1905, 25oz. $570 £300

Silver presentation casket with lightly hammered surface, 5½in. long, by Omar Ramsden, London, 1929.
$645 £320

Unusual cigarette case and lighter combined with enamel Chinese dragon design, late 1920's. $720 £360

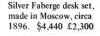

La Minauderie, silver engine-turned evening bag by C. van Cleef and Arpels, about 1935. $970 £480

Silver Faberge desk set, made in Moscow, circa 1896. $4,440 £2,300

Enamelled silver gilt kovsch by Carl Faberge, circa 1913, 7in. long.
$10,450 £5,650

WMF silvered metal tazza, 23.25cm. high, circa 1900. $295 £150

Silver and ivory tazza by Adie Bros. Ltd., 12.75cm. diam., 1930. $505 £260

Attractive Guild of Handicrafts Ltd. silver and enamel tazza, London, 1905, 15.25cm. high. $2,575 £1,300

TEAPOTS

An Eastern silver Art Nouveau teapot, in bulbous gourd form, 8oz. $150 £75

A presentation teapot, inscribed and engraved, by Mappin & Webb, Sheffield, 1896, 4¾in. high, 10oz. 12dwt. $170 £85

Stylish Art Deco teapot in silver coloured metal, 1930's, 11.5cm. high. $250 £130

Hukin & Heath electroplated teapot, 14.5cm. high. $635 £320

Teapot by Christopher Dresser with the London mark for 1880 and marked Ch. Dresser on the body. $1,940 £960

Good A. A. Hebrard teapot, circa 1910, 24cm. high. $25,740 £13,000

SILVER
TEA & COFFEE SETS

Unusual three-piece electroplated coffee service, 1930's. $156 £80

Juventa Art Nouveau electroplated metal coffee service, circa 1900. $194 £100

Small silver teaset, London, 1937, 26¾oz. $200 £100

A silvered teaset of the 1930's. $355 £175

Good Hukin & Heath electroplated picnic set in fitted wood box, 1880. $475 £240

Silver plated tea and coffee service by W.M.F., Germany, 1900. $550 £280

Three-piece silver tea service, London, 1900. $776 £400

Victorian tea and coffee service by J. Round & Sons. $900 £500

A handmade Art Nouveau five-piece silver teaset, Birmingham, 1919, maker's mark DMW, 70¾oz.
$1,060 £525

Four-piece teaset, by John Fetter, Glasgow, 1920-21, 78oz. 10dwt.
$1,045 £580

Guild of Handicrafts silver tea service by C. R. Ashbee, London, 1900-01.
$1,080 £600

Silver five-piece tea and coffee service by Unger Brothers. $1,210 £615

A hand beaten three-piece silver teaset by Omar Ramsden, 29oz. 10dwt., each piece inscribed Omar Ramsden, Me Fecit, 1928. $1,315 £650

Art Deco silver tea service of four-pieces by Jan Puiforcat. $2,020 £1,000

Jensen four-piece coffee set, circa 1930. $2,940 £1,500

Silver teaset and tray by Omar Ramsden and Alwyn Carr, London, 1912-14, 66oz. 18dwt. not including tray.
$3,335 £1,650

Four-piece, lady's plated dressing table set with enamelled mounts. $20 £10

Art Deco silver box, a powder compact, textured lid slashed with red and black enamel. $77 £38

Art Deco enamelled and silver toilet set, circa 1925-30. $265 £140

French enamelled brush set, mirror 24.25cm. high, maker's mark 'JM', 1930's. $335 £180

Late Art Nouveau painted eggshell enamel dressing set signed by N.H. $600 £300

Edwardian silver dressing table service comprising eighteen pieces, including a pair of candlesticks.$2,325 £1,150

One of a pair of Art
Nouveau double-
handled flower vases,
8¾in. high. $90 £45

Art Nouveau silver
flower vase with
pierced and chased
flowers, 9¾in. high,
8oz. $110 £55

Art Nouveau large
circular double-
handled silver flower
vase, 12in. high,
18oz. 10dwt.
$140 £70

James Rogers silver
vase, 14.75cm. high,
Sheffield, 1907.
$195 £100

Jensen silver vase,
London, 1930,
10.25cm. wide.
$315 £170

Puiforcat vase, 1930's,
in silvered coloured
metal, 14.25cm. high.
$405 £220

Puiforcat vase,
11.75cm. high,
1930's.
$480 £260

A fine 'Cymric' vase
by Archibald Knox,
Birmingham, 1902.
$770 £380

One of a pair of Jean
Dunand patinated
metal vases on tripod
bases, circa 1920-25,
25.5cm. high.
$1,073 £580

WOOD

Rowley Gallery gilt wood low relief, circa 1925, 71cm. high. $99 £50

Carved wood sculpture of a woman, 1930's, 95cm. long. $295 £150

Art Deco carved walnut standing figure of a nude girl, stamped N. J. Forrest 1926. $120 £60

Good Hagenauer wood and bronze group of mother and child, 1910-20, 32.5cm. high. $392 £200

Bas relief wood sculpture, by Norman Forrest, 1930's, 93cm. high. $588 £300

Atelier Hagenauer patinated metal and carved wood head, 27cm. high, circa 1920. $590 £320

Good Hagenauer carved wood and bronze figure, 23.5cm. high, 1910-20. $775 £400

Unusual Galle carved and inlaid fruitwood tray, circa 1900. $1,160 £600

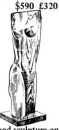

Wood sculpture on slate base, 1930's, 93cm. high. $1,175 £600

122

INDEX

124